TRINITY
COLLEGE LONDON PRESS

C000230444

GRADE **05** PIANO EXTENDED EDITION

21 pieces plus exercises for
Trinity College London
exams 2021-2023

Published by
Trinity College London Press Ltd
trinitycollege.com

Registered in England
Company no. 09726123

Copyright © 2020 Trinity College London Press Ltd
Second impression, August 2021

Cover photograph courtesy of Steinway & Sons

Printed in England by Caligraving Ltd

Performance notes

Coranto / Anon. — Page 7

▶ Renaissance
▶ Articulation
▶ Changing time signatures

'Coranto' takes its name from the word for 'running' and referred to the fast-paced dance that music with this title was written to accompany. The editorial suggestion of 'lively' is certainly appropriate!

The original score of this vivacious piece in the *Fitzwilliam Virginal Book* contains no phrasing, dynamics, fingering, change of time signature or tempo indications. Looking at the editorial suggestions here, the slurring patterns at the beginning help to emphasise the first beat of the bar to strengthen the dance feel, and the dynamics help to highlight the different sections of the piece. However, there are different ways to approach this piece, particularly bearing in mind that it was originally composed for the virginals, a forerunner of the harpsichord and piano. The sound of the virginals was relatively gentle, but the notes did not sustain for very long, and so a relatively detached touch on the piano might be one way to suggest an element of this, and to enhance the rhythmic character of the music.

The change of time signature can also be interpreted in different ways. You might like to think of the minim pulse staying the same – even though that's the same as what's suggested here in mathematical terms, it means you can see a more direct correlation between the two sections. Compare, for example, the first bar of the piece with bars 11 and 12. In the original edition, bars 11 and 12 were combined as one bar – so the first two notes in the top part were minims, exactly as in the first bar of the piece. In other words, the second section is an evolution of the first, with new cross-rhythms introduced in the left hand.

Try to find a recording of this or another Coranto played on a harpsichord or virginals – you'll notice the very different sound generated by the plucking of the strings, giving the music a very rhythmic character.

Allegro / Dušek — Page 8

▶ Classical
▶ Variety of articulation
▶ Phrasing

We often translate 'Allegro' simply as 'quick' or 'fast', but this movement is an excellent example of when 'lively' or 'cheerful' is a much more accurate and appropriate translation.

In conveying this cheerful mood, the score gives us plenty of helpful leads – phrase markings, dynamics, rests, and indications such as *staccato* dots and wedges. You might also like to think a little beyond this too, for example by characterising the opening theme as bold or declamatory,

whereas you might think of the theme that starts in bar 10 as more lyrical in style. Other details can also help to give this piece buoyancy and life, such as the frequent sets of three quavers in the left hand at the ends of bars (eg bars 5 and 6). Perhaps you could imagine each of these notes gains slightly more energy than the previous one, propelling the music towards the next bar – not in terms of tempo, but rather the dynamic and musical intensity. This in turn feeds into the overall feeling of elegance, with each phrase having a distinctive shape, and the music always having a good sense of direction.

When playing piano music from the Classical period, it's worth having a listen to the sound of the fortepiano – the predecessor of the modern piano. With its softer tone that doesn't sustain as well as the modern piano, it gives pieces a gentler, more intimate character.

Valse sentimentale / Schubert — Page 10

▶ Romantic
▶ Expressive playing
▶ Balance: between hands and within chords

Schubert's compositional output is astonishing given his short lifespan, and he wrote several hundreds of dance pieces, including many waltzes. The waltzes in the 'sentimental' collection are particularly appealing, with their expressive character.

The 'sentimental' aspect of this waltz, to a large degree, comes from the repeated resolution of a dissonance, which is first heard in bar 3. Here, the first right-hand chord contains a dissonance (C sharp), before resolving (to B) on the last crotchet of the bar. For the first two times this happens (bars 3 and 5), Schubert marks an accent over the first chord, to emphasise the 'clashing' effect of this chord. By leaning on this chord and then lightening the one that follows, it gives the piece a lilting effect that heightens the usual rhythmic pattern of a waltz, where the first beat in the left hand is stressed. It seems reasonable to assume this accentuation should continue for the rest of the piece.

Schubert gives the indication zart at the beginning, meaning 'tender' or 'delicate', which perfectly encapsulates the style of this beautiful miniature. It's also worth considering two issues of balance in this piece. Firstly, the balance between the hands, where the order of priority is headed up by the right-hand melody, followed by the left-hand bass note, and lastly by the left-hand chords. Secondly, the balance within the right hand, where there are usually at least two parts. Take bars 6-7 as an example, where the quavers in the lower part of the right hand are the main melodic line, before it switches back to the top part in bar 8. You might like to think of this as passing a musical baton between the two parts!

Berceuse / Burgmüller   Page 12

- Romantic
- Lullaby
- Projecting a melody

A Berceuse is a lullaby or cradle song. In this lovely example, the gently flowing semiquavers and steady pulse help create a peaceful atmosphere.

The cantabile marking at the start ('in a singing style') gives a good guide to the importance of the melody in this piece – the notes are marked by the stems that go upwards in the right hand. You might like to think of the piece as a song without words, and perhaps even try singing it to help with the phrasing! Keeping the top of the right-hand as *legato* as possible will help project the tune with a singing tone, rather than relying solely on the sustaining pedal to play smoothly.

Although the metronome mark and tempo indication aren't particularly slow, it might also be helpful to think of the overall pulse as being one dotted crotchet beat per bar. Certainly if you were rocking a baby to sleep to this music, you'd want to use that as your pulse, not the quavers! You can take plenty of time at the two bars marked *rall.*, remembering that the quintuplet in bar 15 is marked *dolce* ('sweetly' or 'softly') – perhaps think of it being rather wistful or thoughtful in character, rather than in any sense fast or virtuosic.

You might like to listen to some other lullabies or cradle songs while preparing this piece. Perhaps the most famous example, and one of the most beautiful, is Brahms' 'Cradle Song'.

Süße Träumerei / Tchaikovsky   Page 15

- Romantic
- Multiple voices in the left hand
- Melody alternates between hands

Following the example of other composers such as Robert Schumann, Tchaikovsky wrote an album of short piano pieces specifically for young performers: *Kinderalbum* or *Album for the Young* was completed in 1878.

As the title suggests, 'Sweet Reverie' has a dream-like quality with a rocking motion in the left hand. Rather than thinking about each note separately, the piece has a continuous, smooth and *legato* sound. The romantic qualities of the piece come from generous and gradual phrases – you could imagine breathing during a deep sleep. You might even want to move your body and allow your own breathing to reflect the lulling pattern of the music.

The pedalling is at the performer's discretion. If used, this technique can support the phrasing but take care not to allow the pedalling to create a muddy sound. Controlling and adjusting the tempo will also help to emphasise moments of tension and relaxation. For example, at the end of sections there is the option to slow down slightly, such as over bars 23-24, 31-32 and 47-48. Issues of tempo and pedalling can also be discussed with your teacher.

You could listen to different recordings of this piece and others by Tchaikovsky to find your own approach.

Pantalon / Beach   Page 18

- Staccato
- Comping in the left hand
- Melody exchanges between hands

Amy Beach was an American composer and pianist and was the first successful American female composer of orchestral music. She wrote *Young People's Carnival* in 1894, which has six pieces all to do with European pantomimes.

This piece musically depicts 'Pantalon', an amusing character deriving from the Italian Commedia dell'arte. The original 1894 edition simply states that the tempo is *Allegro*. While there is some flexibility with the speed of this piece, it is best if it does not drag, in order to convey the lighter, comical tone of the piece.

Amy Beach is believed to have had small hands, so do not worry if your left hand has to jump around a bit in a 'comping' style, as this would have been the case for her too! This motion might even help you embody the jollity of the work. Depending on hand size and comfort, an alternative fingering would be to use finger 5 (right hand) on the third quaver of bar 5 and finger 4 on the first quaver of bar 6, and follow this pattern when this phrase is repeated.

Sports Car / McCabe   Page 21

- Broken chords in left hand
- Long phrases
- Syncopation

'Sports Car' is written by the British composer and pianist, John McCabe, who has written in pretty much every genre there is. Much of his music uses repeating patterns to achieve continuity and drive.

This piece has a perpetual sense of motion, resulting in a driving, smooth and continuous sound. The repeating patterns in the left hand could depict the road underneath this sports car and the constantly changing landscape.

The balance between hands is one of the trickier aspects of this piece. The score indicates the left-hand part should be played *staccato* throughout, resulting in a sense of drive, but you might not want these to be too intrusive and take a more 'back-seat' role to the melody. It might be a good idea to make an exercise out of playing the left and right-hand parts separately to help build independence between them. There is a car horn sound over bars 35-42 and you could choose to place a slight accent on these off-beat clusters to emphasise the fun character. Above all, you are encouraged to relax and enjoy the ride!

Large Wave / Pam Wedgwood   Page 24

- Arabesque texture
- Use of free tempo
- Playing in high registers

'Large Wave' is by the British composer and pianist Pam Wedgwood. Much of her music is in a Jazz style and is usually descriptive, musically illustrating a scene or image.

Like many pieces about the sea and waves, this piece has flowing lines, smooth phrases and a sense of ebb and flow, like large oceanic waves. There is a good amount of freedom with the tempo – in fact, the beginning does not specify a metronome marking, although it does give a mood. Here, the tempo is at the performer's discretion, although you may choose to make this broadly consistent with later passages, where the tempo is indicated. On the other hand, from bar 13 – where the introduction comes back – could return to a freer tempo, before moving into a more regular rhythm once again from bar 18. Relax into these phrases, making full use of the expression through the dynamics and broad phrases, as the music moves in large breaths.

March of the Roman Legionaries / Gerou   Page 26

▶ Contemporary
▶ Rhythmic precision
▶ Ternary form (ABA)

The constant, rhythmic tramp of Roman soldiers on the march is portrayed in this characterful piece by American composer and piano teacher Tom Gerou. There's a flavour of Grieg's 'In the Hall of the Mountain King' in the menacing tread of this piece, and the direction to play 'with sarcasm' offers scope for interpretation and musical shaping.

Accurate tempo and rhythmic precision are important in creating and maintaining the narrative of the music. Be sure to articulate the notes as marked as the changes in articulation give the music forward-drive and character. Crisp *staccato*, using a 'plucked' finger motion and strong upward lift out of the keyboard, and percussive accents where marked will enhance the drama of the music.

Notice how the dynamic level increases gradually, rising to *forte* in bar 19, to create the impression of the army getting closer. Now they are visible in all their regalia, marching through the town, and the middle B section needs a confident, full sound to portray this. While the left hand underpins the melody, the right hand has some jumps to negotiate. Make use of the rests to move the hand into the new position to ensure that you land on the next phrase accurately. From bar 36, as the right hand moves up the register, so the dynamic level drops and the piece ends *p*, as the legionaries' footsteps fade into the distance.

Settle Down / Goodwin   Page 29

▶ Jazz
▶ Syncopated rhythms
▶ Jazz harmonies

American composer Gordon Goodwin is also a musician and bandleader, and this piece suggests the sound of big band jazz. Imagine the right hand as a saxophone or trumpet, accompanied by trombones, bass and rhythm section, and aim for a full, 'brassy' sound, especially in the chords.

Swing the quavers to enhance the jazz vibe of the music and drop the hand into the chords using the weight of your wrist to create a full sound, especially in the accented chords. To do this accurately, learn the chords carefully so that both your fingers and ear know their shape and sound.

Careful counting is important throughout with so many off-beat notes and syncopated rhythms. The middle section of the piece (from bar 17) is more settled and quieter in mood, providing a good contrast to the previous page. Keep the right-hand chords relaxed and lightly spring between them here to create a soft *staccato*. The left hand sustained, tied notes suggest the long sounds of a trombone so balance your touch and sound to achieve a nice resonance under the melody. At bar 27, the full brassy sound of the big band returns so give these chords power and highlight the stressed notes in the left hand in bars 29 and 30 with plenty of punch (that trombone again!). Enjoy the final jazz chord and its unusual sound and don't be tempted to release the notes too soon.

Typhoon / Petot   Page 32

▶ Contemporary jazz
▶ Changing time signatures
▶ Expression

American composer Ross Petot is also a stride pianist (stride is a type of jazz). There are some elements of stride piano in 'Typhoon' and you might find it helpful to listen to music by jazz pianists such as Thelonius Monk and Duke Ellington to get a flavour of the sound, rhythms and mood.

A typhoon is a tropical storm and in this atmospheric piece the powerful wind and waves are portrayed in the arpeggios which 'roll up' the keyboard. These are marked *legato* and without the help of pedal (the composer is quite specific about this) so you will need secure fingering to enable you to play them smoothly. In bars 9 and 10 treat the arpeggios as a single gesture, even though they are shared between the hands, and try to create the impression of one hand playing.

At bar 11 the time signature changes, with the direction to retain the same quaver metre through the $\frac{6}{8}$ passages. Here, the forceful repeated left-hand notes and the descending chromatic quavers in the right create a sense of urgency and drama before the opening section returns.

At bar 24 the $\frac{6}{8}$ section reappears, though now changed slightly and with a *diminuendo* and *rit.* the music suggests the storm is dying back, only to return even more forcefully in the last line. Give those final Gs plenty of punch – using the second or third finger will give you the control to create a big, bold sound.

Walk in the Park / Fox   Page 34

▶ Contemporary
▶ Syncopated rhythms
▶ Expression

This appealing, cheerful piece by Gilon Fox illustrates an enjoyable stroll in the park during which your attention may be caught by all the myriad sights and sounds of nature and wildlife. The syncopations suggest the start-stop progress of the walk, and the piece is infused with jazz harmonies, with some unexpectedly 'crunchy' chords which are highlighted by accents.

Don't be alarmed by the $\frac{12}{8}$ time signature. This is the compound time equivalent of $\frac{4}{4}$ and here the beat is marked by a dotted crotchet. The music moves forward with a 'relaxed swagger' and careful counting will ensure the off-beat notes come in at the right time.

In the middle section, the left-hand accompaniment becomes more bluesy in style – you may wish to give these notes greater weight (imagine the resonant sound of a double bass player plucking those left-hand notes) as they add colour and interest especially where the right hand has sustained chords. The piece combines *legato* and *staccato* articulation so bring plenty of contrast to each. Equally, dynamics should be well-defined as these enhance the character of the piece.

Authors: Martin Ford, Owen Burton and Frances Wilson

[Blank page to facilitate page turns]

Coranto

no. 221 from *Fitzwilliam Virginal Book*

Anon.
ed. James Long

Allegro

1st movt from *Sonata XII in G major*

František Xaver Dušek
(1731-1799)

Omit the repeat in the exam.

Valse sentimentale

op. 50 no. 13

Franz Schubert
(1797-1828)

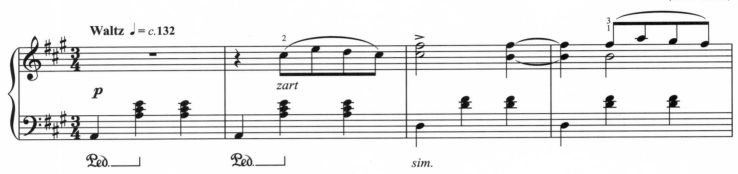

Omit the repeat in the exam.

Berceuse

no. 7 from *18 Characteristic Studies*, op. 109

Friedrich Burgmüller
(1806–1874)

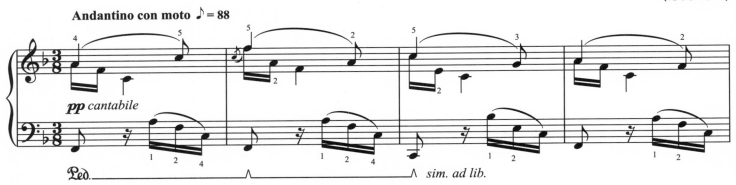

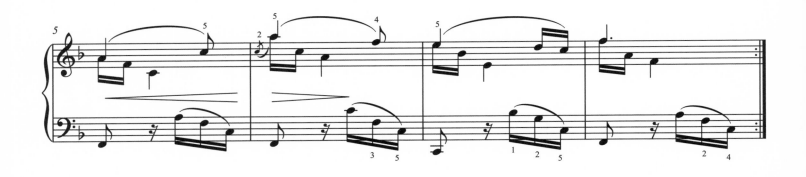

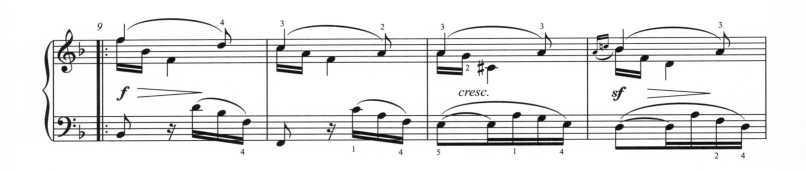

Omit the repeats in the exam.

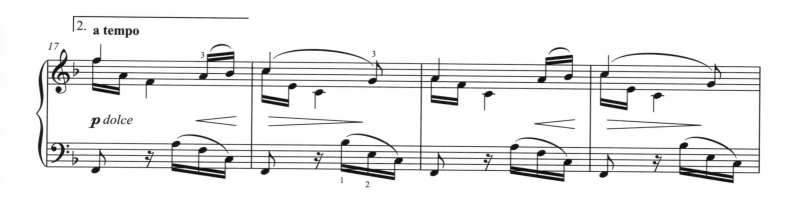

[Blank page to facilitate page turns]

Süße Träumerei (Sweet Reverie)

no. 21 from *Kinderalbum*, op. 39

Pyotr Ilyich Tchaikovsky
(1840–1893)

Pantalon

from *Young People's Carnival*, op. 25

Amy Beach
(1867–1944)
ed. Maurice Hinson

20

Sports Car

John McCabe
(1939-2015)

Large Wave

Pam Wedgwood
(b. 1947)

Omit the repeats in the exam.

March of the Roman Legionaries

Tom Gerou

[Blank page to facilitate page turns]

Settle Down

Gordon Goodwin
(b. 1954)

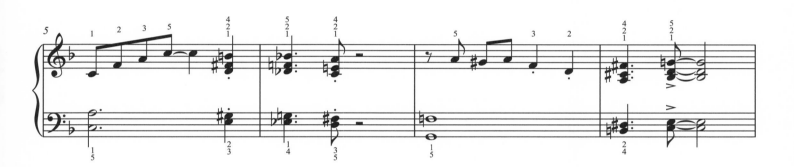

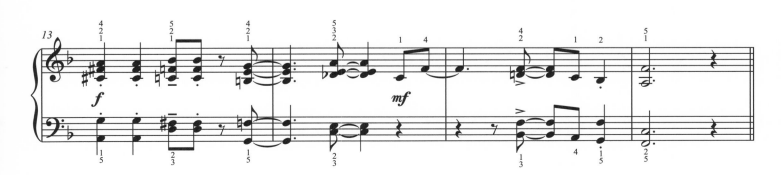

29

31

Typhoon

Ross Petot
(b. 1957)

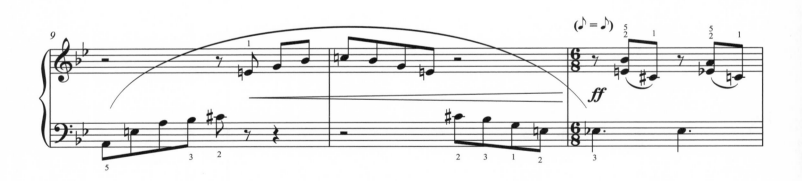

From *Moods and Impressions, Book 2* (WP1190), by Ross Petot. Reprinted with permission 2020 - www.kjos.com

Walk in the Park

Gilon Fox
(b. 2004)

Exercises

1a. Gentle Waves – tone, balance and voicing

1b. Dancing Shoes – tone, balance and voicing

2a. Joining the Dots – co-ordination

2b. Topsy-turvy – co-ordination

3a. Village Hop – finger & wrist strength and flexibility

3b. Broadway – finger & wrist strength and flexibility

Scales and arpeggios

The fingering given in this book is offered as a recommendation only. Any other logical system of fingering is acceptable provided that it is consistent and allows an even execution of the requirements.

Please note that the recommended speeds are a guide to what can be expected at each level. For the purposes of fulfilling exam criteria, accuracy, fluency and evenness of touch and tone should be regarded as equally important aspects of technical competence.

1. Scales (from memory) – Examiners select from the following:					
D♭ and B major	min. ♩ = 110	*f* or *p*	legato or staccato	two octaves	hands together
B♭ and G♯ minor (candidate's choice of *either* harmonic *or* melodic minor)					
G harmonic minor contrary motion scale					
Chromatic scale in similar motion starting on D♭					
Chromatic scale in contrary motion, left hand starting on C and right hand starting on E			legato only		
2. Arpeggios (from memory, in similar motion) – Examiners select from the following:					
D♭ and B major	min. ♩ = 90	*f* or *p*	legato or staccato	two octaves	hands together
B♭ and G♯ minor					
Diminished 7th starting on B					

D♭ major scale

D♭ major arpeggio (two octaves)

B major scale (two octaves)

B major arpeggio (two octaves)

B♭ minor scale: harmonic (two octaves)

B♭ minor scale: melodic (two octaves)

B♭ minor arpeggio (two octaves)

G# minor scale: harmonic (two octaves)

G♯ minor scale: melodic (two octaves)

G♯ minor arpeggio (two octaves)

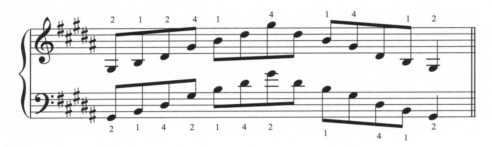

G minor scale: harmonic, contrary motion (two octaves)

Diminished 7th starting on B (two octaves)

Chromatic scale in similar motion starting on D♭ (two octaves)

Chromatic scale in contrary motion starting on C and E, *legato* only (two octaves)